Footprints

By Dorothy Ferguson

How very softly
you tiptoed into my world.
Almost silently,
only for a moment you stayed.
But what an imprint
your footsteps have left
upon my heart.

A note from Dorothy. . .

Once in a lifetime, or maybe more, an individual enters our lives in a precious and powerful way. For some of us, the special person stays for only a moment. For others, longer. For some that child is only a brief dream, than a bittersweet memory. But each of us is somehow aware that we have experienced a small presence that will not leave us unchanged.

This memory book is tenderly dedicated to the special presence of the many infants and young children who have quietly or no-so-quietly passed our way. It is yours to write in, create poems in, and place precious pictures and memories throughout. If you like, a copy of your baby's little footprints can be pasted over those on the cover.

Our thanks to all of the special parents who shared their miles to help create *Little Footprints*
and to the people who shared their grief.

A Special Dedication:
to the memory of Colin Michael Galloway, who was stillborn November 2, 1983

Phone: 866-218-0101

Email: centeringcorp@aol.com

www.centering.org

CENTERING CORPORATION
AND
GRIEF DIGEST MAGAZINE
GRIEF RESOURCES

This page is for a copy of your baby's footprints,
a picture, or anything special to give you a precious memory.
(These small suggestions are intended to be covered up)

You have set my feet in a very large place. –Psalm 31

You are so beautiful to me!
A page of photographs of our baby.

Ideas:
Hospital or ultrasound photos,
pictures of Mommy before baby was born.

Your Story: The Day You Were Born

What we expected while we were expecting you, our dreams and our hopes.
This is your story before your short life ended.

What we did when we learned we were expecting you:

Your name and how we came to choose it:

Date of your delivery:

Time of your birth:

Time of your death:

Your Doctor and special staff people who cared for us:

You were so precious.

You were   inches long.

You weighed   .

And we remember you with love in our hearts.

Last Moments

Date of your death:

The day:

Hour:

Place:

Things I will always remember:

It is amazing that the rest of the world just keeps going on.
How can that be when our very life has been so changed in only a moment?

You were here only a short time, but your family will love you forever.

Your Mother

Your Mother's name:

Her date of birth:

Place where she was born:

Your sisters and brothers:

Your Mommy's Parents:

Her Grandparents:

Other family members who would have been important to you:

You are ours. You belong to us.

Your Mother

This is what I would have liked you to know about your Mommy:

Oh Young Thing, your mother's lovely armful. –Euripides

Your Father

Your Father's name:

His date of birth:

Place where he was born:

Your Daddy's Parents:

His Grandparents:

Other family members who would have loved you:

We think you would have looked a lot like:

I could hold you in my hand. Now I hold you in my heart.

Your Father

This is what I would have liked you know about your Daddy:

Although the day is not mine to give, I will show you in the morning sun. –David Welton

Your Grandparents

Here is what you would want to know about your Grandparents:

We love you, even though you could not stay.

What else was going on in the world
A page for newspaper clippings -
and a clipping about you or a note of how we told people of your birth and death:

And in that vastness,
the horrible dryness of the plains,
they buried their children.

Alone.

Desolate.

The chill winds turning their capes and coats
into a fury to match their grief.
They were the pioneers.
And the new land was marked
with the graves of their young.

A Time For Remembering and Honoring You

Date of your memorial service:

What we did:

What we did with your tiny body:

People who shared with us:

With music:

With special words:

With flowers and gifts:

There are no words, there is only love.

People who came by, called and sent notes -

Good people who brought food, flowers, and did things that helped us

And so they gave me what they could.
They shed a gentle tear.

I have some things
that need to be packed away:
blankets, jammies, shirts
and one special bear with a music box.
But I don't know how to even begin
to pack away all these dreams.

What am I to do
with the hopes and the plans
for all the tomorrows?

A Journal of Thoughts and Feelings

Six months after your death:

At certain seasons,
the eternal child within me
longs for you.

A Journal of Thoughts and Feelings

The first holiday after your death:

A Journal of Thoughts and Feelings

The first anniversary of your death:

Tonight I will light a very small candle.
It will be warm and moving. And I will think of you.
Tonight.

At unusual times,

in unexpected places:

the supermarket, the ball game,

on the way home from work,

my eyes sting and my throat gets tight.

And then I know

that all I want

is you.

This is hard to understand.
I had so many dreams for you.
I've wondered how I'd feel
when you learned to say my name and yours.
I've thought about the day
when you would start school.

I guess I'll think about you
when the leaves begin to change
or when I see a snowflake land
on someone's stocking cap.
It's hard to know that it will never be.

I hurt inside.
I've missed you now, already.
It's hard to understand.

In fact, I don't.

A Journal of Thoughts and Feelings

A page of feelings, thoughts and remembering:

I have so many special feelings deep inside.
Some I'd like to share. Some I'd like to hide.
There are so many special feelings inside today.
They are my own. They are ok.

Keepsakes

That special note, a lock of hair, your hospital bracelet, birth and death announcements, perhaps another picture that will let us keep you in our hearts forever.

Thank you -
for the gift of you. You gave us hope by just being you!
After the hurting and healing are through,
we'll treasure most of all, the gift of you.

In the years to come, I will not forget you -

She would be ten now. . .
And I wonder, would she have dancing curls and sparkling eyes and a dimple in her cheek like her mother?

She would be ten now. . .
Perhaps too old for laps but not too old to be tucked in at night and kissed and told not to let the bedbugs bite.

She would be ten now. . .
Daddy's little girl, full of ideas, opinions and laughter.

We lost her ten years ago. She was our first child. She was our last child. We had awaited her with eager expectation. I bought a crib and sanded it down myself and repainted it in the garage. We painted the room and it became a child's room with a cute little lamp. But that room would never hold a child, nor would we. We made many mistakes, but we were on a road without maps and did not know the way.

We didn't name her. We had decided to call our first baby girl Emily. But when we had this broken child who lived only four hours, we told the nurses just to call her Baby Girl on the certificates that marked her birth and her death. We have since given her back her name and mourned her death and celebrated her brief life. She was a real child, her loss a real loss. Her birth was a real birth, her death a real death.

We did not see her. You see, she was badly broken and in our brokenness we did not think we had the strength to look on hers. I have since seen such broken babies. I have held them, and I have watched their mothers hold them as they quietly slipped from this world into the next where God would hold them for eternity.

We did not have other children. We felt the risk too high, the pain too great. Now, as we have grown into middle age, we wish we had taken the risk. No, the healthy ones will not replace the broken ones. Each is as unique as their fingerprints. Subsequent children will never take the place of the child you have lost, but other children will fill a place in your heart - not the lost child's place, but another place waiting to be filled.

She would be ten now. . .Not a day goes by that I do not think of her, wonder about her, try to picture her in my mind. Losing a child is not something you will get over, but it is something you will get through, and something you can grow through as well as go through. When I think of Emily now and her name is whispered down the corridors of my dreams, it is less often with sorrow and more often with joy. . .joy that someday we will see her in that kingdom where all brokenness will be healed, all tears wiped away, and the eternal afternoon of laughter will begin. I see her there now, and she is ten.

By Rev. Terry Morgan from the book, *Dear Parents, letters to and from bereaved parents*, Centering Corporation.
Emily died shortly after birth from anacephaly.

By Dorothy Ferguson

At quiet times
When there's just me,
I wonder what it will be like
To let go of some of the old feelings.

I wonder if letting go
Will seem disloyal to you.

Or if it will be like a raw wound
That is beginning to heal.